Self-Love, Family, Health, Gratitude, and Kindness.

KEEP GOING,
Keep Growing

Wellness journal with a 70-Day Tracker to help you
continue to grow into the best version of yourself

PATTY BARAJAS GODINEZ

Printed in the United States of America

Published in Hellertown, PA

Cover design by Leanne Coppola

Author photo and page 9 photos by Julie Whitaker

Library of Congress Control Number 202 2920189

ISBN 978-1-958711-23-1

2 4 6 8 10 9 7 5 3 1

For more information or to place bulk orders, contact the author or the publisher at Jennifer@BrightCommunications.net.

Bright
COMMUNICATIONS

BrightCommunications.net

To anyone who's ever said "I'll start Monday."
Today is a good day to fight for a better you,
and 70 days from now you'll be grateful you started today.

CONTENTS

INTRODUCTION

We all know that self-care is something we should do, but it's always the first thing we neglect. Life is crazy busy, and we are often scrambling to find time.

Over the years, I have implemented new habits to get me to where I am, and where I am headed. I discovered that the more positive habits I worked on, the more extra time I found. All of these changes have been the glue that has held me together and allowed me to grow—in spite of the challenging days. I wanted to feel happy, healthy, brave, and accomplished, all while giving more than I take. I also wanted my three kids to move their bodies, eat healthier, and be kind, giving humans. You can't ask someone to do something you are not willing to do, which is why modeling the behavior was the best thing I could have ever done.

I don't pretend to know the secrets to life, but I do know that when you change your mindset and incorporate good habits, you change your life. I will always be a work in progress because there's always something that needs improvement. I'm sharing what worked for me in hopes that it empowers you to make yourself a priority. Start and end your day on a positive note by taking some time to practice gratitude and reflect on what went right and what went wrong, and make adjustments as you go. We all get 24 hours in a day and focusing 1 hour for ourselves really does make all the difference. It is completely possible to change the things you want to change.

I designed this journal to be a 70-day process because I want you to fully commit. In that time, you will build habits that will stay with you long after the 70 days. I want to see others rise, grow, and expand, and my hope is that this wellness journal is a step closer to help you become who you want to be, while building a sustainable routine that doesn't take away from the people who need you. In fact, if you implement some of these changes into your life, you'll stop putting yourself on the back burner, and almost like magic, you will have more to give to those who surround you.

It's a fact that the butterfly goes through an extreme transformation to become her true self. The process is difficult, and it takes time and consumes a great deal of energy, but it's part of the journey for the butterfly to change into something beautiful. Had she not decided to fight for her life and reach her full potential, she would never know that she was created to fly.

GROWTH PILLAR #1

Mindset

In my home, we are constantly talking about filling our cup. My youngest daughter is a very visual person. This is how I explained to her the importance of keeping our cups full.

- The pitcher filled with water represents all the goodness in the world: love, confidence, positivity, happiness, support, and all the goodness that we have to give.
- The large bowl represents your family: your partner, kids, parents, siblings, cousins, friends, coworkers, and everyone else who surrounds you.
- The cup, well, you are the cup.

What happens when you fill up your cup with all that goodness?! You pour water into your cup, and because you are a mother/father, a wife/husband, a daughter/son, a sibling, a friend, and an employee, you slowly start to give all that goodness away. You give it away until your cup is empty.

Sure, you are going to have days when you fill up again. You are going to work on self-care and build more love, confidence, and positivity, and your cup is going to fill up again, but because you are a giver, you are going to give it all away again. You give a little more here, a little more there, and eventually your cup is going to be empty again.

Some days your cup may even tip over and shatter. We all have our breaking point. I had mine in 2017, when everything seemed to be going wrong, and I realized I had to make a change. So, I started giving myself some love. I started working out, reading, eating better, hydrating, sleeping, making intentional time with my family, building mental toughness, and staying consistent with self-care. I worked on myself every single morning without fail, and because I did that, my cup was full. Not only was my cup full, but it was spilling over to the bowl, and all of the people who surround me began benefitting from all that goodness. I had so much more to give because I was finally taking care of myself.

As parents, we sometimes feel that it's selfish to do anything for ourselves. Oftentimes we feel like we are taking away from our kids. It took me most of my life to finally realize that the more

I have, the more I can give. Our kids don't need perfect parents; they need *happy* parents. They need to see that we also matter. If they see that, when they grow up and they feel stuck, they'll be able remember back and do what they saw worked for us. Taking care of ourselves gives us more energy to run around with them, it gives us more patience, it teaches them how to fuel their bodies with healthy foods, and it models for them the importance of self-care. You can't give what you don't have. Let's work on filling our cups!

GROWTH PILLAR #2

Habits

Habits are behaviors that you perform automatically, like flipping the light switch on every time you walk into a room or brushing your teeth every morning. They're routines you get through without having to think about much.

I'm pretty sure it was a struggle when you were first introduced to the "bunny ears" to learn how to tie your shoes. However, after practicing the skill for some time, it became second nature. Now you tie your shoes every single day with no effort at all. In order to build new habits and make them a part of who we are, we have to keep repeating the behavior.

It can be difficult to get started on something when you don't have any direction. Everyone is different, and we all require different support systems. Start by implementing small habits that you can build on over time. Here are six habits I worked on consistently that changed my life:

- <u>Movement:</u> I started working out 30 minutes a day consistently. I modified, I used my own body weight, and I took breaks when I needed them. As difficult as it was, I kept going until I finished what I said I would do. When I gained more strength, balance, and flexibility, I started to build more faith in myself, and I slowly incorporated weights. That inspired me to do more challenging workouts and increase my workout time. It was a huge change from being glued to my couch, but I knew that every little step was molding me into the kind of person I wanted to be.

- <u>Nutrition:</u> I started observing how certain foods made me feel. I filled my plate with more veggies, proteins, fruits, and healthier carbs and fats. I cut back on sugary drinks and fast food. Portion control became my new normal. It wasn't about giving up any food groups. It was more about learning how to fuel my body with the proper nutrition. Doing that kept me satisfied and gave me more energy. I am a lover of anything chocolate, and I still enjoy my treats in moderation.

- <u>Hydration:</u> I started drinking half my body weight in ounces of water daily. I carried a water bottle with me at all times, making it a visible reminder to keep drinking. Sometimes we think we are hungry when in fact, we are just thirsty. My mood improved, I was more focused and alert, my face cleared up, my digestion improved, and I was flushing out all the toxins from my body. Doing this also kept me from thinking I was hungry all day.

- Sleep: I was a night owl and struggled with insomnia for more than a decade. Not sleeping led to exhaustion, brain fog, forgetfulness, and overeating. I was always running on fumes. I scheduled my exercise at 4:00 in the morning, which made me tired by the time the sun went down. I stopped all electronic use one hour before bed. During the day, I chased the sun for extra melatonin and started winding down at least an hour before my bedtime. A rested body provides better quality work and better performance and heals faster after physical or mental exertion.

- Gratitude: I started writing down three things that I am grateful for. At the end of my day, I sit in complete silence and write all about the three things that happened during my day. I focus on the good things and turn failures into lessons. Doing this little habit consistently over time has made me a more positive person. I often find myself looking for positive things throughout my day. You know what happens when you look? You find them! There is always something to be grateful for.

- Personal development: I upgraded my mindset and became the kind of person who starts the day on a positive note. Every morning, I read 10 pages from a self-help book. I take notes and highlight passages that resonate with me. Reading and soaking in books that could help me become a better version of myself was life-changing. It's also nice to go back to my notes and highlights when I am struggling. Every time I go back, I catch something I missed the first time around. This simple daily habit has made me more resilient and open to new opportunities.

I'm not saying that change was easy. I struggled, more often than not, but I kept going. I had every excuse in the book to not do what I said I would do. In the end, my WHY was much bigger than any excuse I had, and I had plenty of them.

GROWTH PILLAR #3
Your Why

Your WHY is the force behind what you do. Understanding why you're doing what you're doing is an important factor to have a chance at success. Knowing why we are doing the hard work will push us beyond our capabilities. What we do matters to someone, and forgetting that can easily make us feel uninspired and discouraged. Never underestimate what can be achieved by writing things down. Your thoughts, dreams, visions, and goals all have the ability to become your reality. Post your WHY in a visible place to remind you to keep pushing, especially on the hard days.

My family is *my* WHY—my standing pillars and the lights of my world. They are the reason I finally decided to start taking care of myself, for my happiness and theirs. Dedicating time for myself makes me a better wife, mom, and daughter and all-around better person. I aim to be the best, most genuine version of myself—not only on the outside, but on the inside where it counts the most. After all, how can I raise happy kids if I can't show them what it means to be happy?! We all need a WHY to motivate and inspire us.

What is your WHY?

_____

_____

_____

_____

_____

_____

_____

"Happiness comes from what we do. Fulfillment comes from WHY we do it."
—Simon Sinek

GROWTH PILLAR #4

Self-Love

Believing in my ability to control my life has increased my confidence and self-worth. It has helped me put myself out there to try new things and have confidence in my own abilities. Consistency is what made all the difference. I went from always quitting on myself to proving every day that I matter.

I've had to put a lot of work into learning how to love myself. It's not just about standing in front of the mirror and telling myself that I am beautiful. It's more about acceptance, understanding, and implementing habits that give me courage, confidence, and strength. Self-care is not selfish.

Schedule time to focus on your needs. This includes anything you do to make yourself healthy and happy—physically, mentally, emotionally, and spiritually. Practicing self-care helps eliminate stress, depression, anxiety, and burnout. The more time you spend charging your batteries, the more positive energy you will have for the people who surround you.

"You are not smart enough. You are not strong enough. You are not capable." You wouldn't say these words to your kids or anyone you love. Why say them to yourself?! We are our own biggest critics. When we have these negative thoughts long enough, we actually start to believe them. Self-doubt can completely stop us from trying.

Be kind to yourself and love yourself just as much as you love those around you. When your friends have bad days, you do whatever you can to build them up. Be a friend to yourself. Celebrate your strengths, focus on your positive qualities, and forgive yourself. We all know what we are good at and also what we need to work on. Stop with the negative chatter and celebrate the good stuff.

- Take care of your mind, body, and soul.
- Surround yourself with positive people.
- Face your fears.
- Don't compare yourself to others.

- Recharge your batteries.

- Treat yourself to something nice.

- Extend a helping hand to someone in need.

- Always express what you feel.

- Sleep whenever possible.

- Make time to meditate and unwind.

- Do something every day that brings you joy.

Life gets busy, and sometimes we have to remove a few things from our plate to make room for the unexpected. In my experience, that usually ended up being something I had planned for myself. Build faith in yourself by sticking to your plans as best as you can. Don't fail to do what you said you would do. The things we say to ourselves are powerful, and they will shape who we become. Don't get to the point where you lose all faith in yourself. Make yourself a priority.

Forget about thinking that you have to look and be perfect. Happiness comes from self-acceptance and acknowledging our strengths and weaknesses. It doesn't matter what you look like, but rather what your body is capable of doing. Don't take for granted that you can go on a nice walk and embrace the sun. Many people don't have the ability to do that without pain.

Life is never going to be perfect, and it doesn't have to be. Having confidence improves how you feel about yourself, and it also helps you better understand and love others.

GROWTH PILLAR #5
Family and Parenting

I love my kids more anything in this world. Just like everyone else, I have my days of doubt. I sometimes wonder if I know what I am even doing with my little humans. We all have different types of days as parents: the unbelievable, magical, hectic, inspiring, overwhelming, supportive, no patience, loving, screaming, happy, sad, and fulfilling days. We will continue to show up when we are sad, tired, and disappointed.

I have yet to meet the perfect parent. The truth is: We don't have to have it together all the time. We just have to do our best. We raise our kids to be good people, and in the end we hope that we've taught them enough to grow into responsible, kind, loving adults.

Let's give ourselves permission and grace to do things our way, to make mistakes, and to learn from them. Let's work on filling our cup so that we have more courage to get through the days ahead. Most importantly, let's support one another. Life is hard enough already, and I truly believe we are all doing the best we can.

Keep in mind what we learned in kindergarten, "If you don't have anything nice to say, don't say anything at all." We can't see into the future, and we don't know who our children will become. Don't judge other parents and put yourself in a vulnerable position that may easily be attacked one day. Be kind, helpful, supportive, and willing to love, especially when you see other parents going through a rough season.

Being a parent doesn't mean you have to put yourself on the back burner. You matter, your marriage matters, and your relationships matter, too! Date nights are very common before marriage, but they are more crucial *during* marriage. I know it can be a challenge to get out the door when you have young kids at home. I've been there. It requires babysitters and planning ahead, but it can also involve doing something very inexpensive. Make some time for yourself as a couple, away from your kids and all the responsibilities. Get dressed up, change it up, and leave all the worries at home. We all need a break away from our kids to communicate, catch up, feel more connected, and support each other on this rollercoaster ride called life.

Children learn from observing their parents. There's a lot of things I'm doing wrong as a parent, but I will never stop trying. Showing my kids how much I love, value, and appreciate my husband is top priority. A strong bond between parents is the heart of a happy family. A strong relationship will provide security for your kids and show them what a loving, respectful relationship looks like. What could possibly be more important than that?!

Here are some changes we made to strengthen our relationship:

- We made intentional time with our family a priority by scheduling time on our calendar for group dates and one-on-one time.

- We turned off electronics to remove distractions and have more time to create memories. I can't recommend this enough.

- We made date night a priority. Our marriage also needs time to recharge. It's important to communicate and build a happy and peaceful relationship.

- We started scheduling a family meeting every Sunday evening. This helped us review our plans for the week, opened up the communication with our kids, and helped us connect as a family.

- Dinner at the table became a priority for our family. It's the only time when we are all together in one place. We started cooking together and discussing everything that happened throughout our day. It has also created better eating habits. (Kids are more likely to eat veggies when they eat with the entire family.)

- My daily walk turned into a *family* walk. It's amazing the amount of conversations you can have on a 45-minute walk. This was huge for time management because we were able to spend intentional time as a family while getting some movement in.

- A few years back, I started writing letters to my kids every month. In those letters, I tell them how much I love them and how grateful I am to have them. I talk about events, accomplishments, trips, and memories we made that month. My kids read their letters, seal them, and file them in their letter chest. One day, when I am gone, they'll each have their chest filled with hundreds of memories, pictures, and words from their mom. Say what you need to say now. Don't leave anything for tomorrow.

> *"You teach someone to read 10 pages of a book a day, and chances*
> *are you may see how it changes her, but chances are you won't see*
> *how it changes her kids, and her kids' friends, and their friends."*
> —*Jeff Olson*

GROWTH PILLAR #6

Kindness

Kindness starts with being kind to yourself and creating the ripple effect. Compassion and generosity travel both directions, and most people will pay it forward by doing good things for others. The truth is, everyone can use a little kindness in their world. We never know what someone might be going through. That doesn't mean we have to wait until something bad happens to make them feel good. Start today!

Right around the time I started teaching my kids to share their toys, I started teaching them to be givers. I wasn't *telling* them to give; I was walking the walk. I was a mess as far as taking care of myself, but one thing I have always done is generously give my time and energy to the people who I love. It's one of many things I learned from watching my mom. Every time I do something kind for someone, I make it a point to involve my kids. Now it lights up my world when they go out of their way to bake, pick flowers, write a card, or wrap up a gift for someone.

- Developing healthy habits will create more kindness toward others. You treat people better when you take care of yourself.

- Do things without expecting anything in return. Every morning after I finish my workout, I sit for a few minutes and think of how I could sprinkle kindness into the world. Sometimes it comes in the form of a sweet surprise for someone I know, and other days it is an act of kindness for a complete stranger.

- Surprising people lifts the soul. You never know when someone could use the support and encouraging words.

- Write an email or send a text to someone thanking them for the impact they have made in your life.

<u>Non-appearance compliments that speak to the soul:</u>
- You are making a difference.
- You inspire me.

- I love how passionate you are.
- You are brave.
- You make the world a better place.
- You light up a room.
- Your energy is contagious.
- I admire your courage.
- You make me feel happy.
- The world would feel empty without you.

Gifts that don't cost a dime:
- Apologize when you are wrong
- Share what you have
- Do something unexpected for someone
- Comfort during difficult times
- Encourage
- Lend a listening ear
- Be patient
- Be consistent
- Help them take action
- Send a sweet message

Imagine a world where everyone woke up and thought about one kind thing they could do for someone else…

"The average person makes 35,000 choices each day, and every one of them,
big or small, can shape our ability to be kind, patient,
and committed people. Character is a habit."
—Houston Kraft

GROWTH PILLAR #7
Time Management

For years, I thought it was selfish to make some time for myself. Something else always needed my attention, and time was always running from me. My husband was working 12-hour night shifts, I was working full-time, my three kids were attending three different schools in three different locations, and they were involved in many different sports and extracurricular activities.

When all you do is give, you don't have the chance to recharge your own batteries. If you want to take care of others, start by taking care of yourself. It's impossible to share a resource with others that we ourselves are lacking.

"I don't have time."
—Everyone

- Make a detailed list for an entire week of everything you do. When you review it at the end of the week, you'll see where most of your time is going. My list included way too much Netflix. Nothing wrong with that, but I now save it for the end of the day when I am completely done with my priorities. Tracking everything I was doing helped me make the proper adjustments to make more room for the things that I needed. I discovered a lot of lost time doing things that were not benefiting me.

- Learn to kindly say "no" to be able to say "yes" to things that are going to help you grow. It's okay to say "no" when you have prior commitments. Overcommitting can be overwhelming. It's important to be honest about what you can handle.

- Ask for help when you need it. Asking for help can be difficult because it can hurt our pride or makes us feel like we are not capable. In my experience, asking for help has created better results. Asking my family for help around the house gave us more time for the things that really matter. Reaching out for support helped me gain a better perspective and great advice. We don't have all the answers, and sometimes we need support. Having the courage to ask for help is not a weakness. It's true strength when we are willing to admit that we are struggling.

- Do your most difficult task first thing in the morning. You are more likely to complete it when you feel you have time on your side. As the day progresses, you start coming up with excuses on why you shouldn't do it. That's exactly why I schedule my workout and personal development before the sun comes up.

- Write down everything that is in your head—groceries to buy, errands to run, or things you need to do for your kids. This will help you clear your mind, get organized, and feel a sense of control to be more productive with your time.

Your time belongs to you! You are in control!

THE TRACKER

It's up to us to follow through and push through our struggles. Trackers are a good way to measure what we do, and they hold us accountable. We all want to feel like we accomplished what we planned, and checking off, circling, and scratching off helps us celebrate those moments.

In the daily tracker, you will find a scoring of 1 through 5 for your daily habits. (5 being the highest success.) Everyone is different, therefore everyone will have different goals, and success will look different for everyone. You will set your own standards on what you want to accomplish and circle how you feel you did. Be honest; don't cheat yourself.

Movement: Whether it's doing two workouts a day, one high intensity workout, yoga, stretching, or taking a 30 minute walk, you decide where you want to start and make adjustments when you feel ready to increase.

Read 10 pages: Choose any book that is going to inspire you and help you grow. This could be a book on parenting, confidence, marriage, finances, faith, habits, health, mindset, nutrition, or discipline. You will become unstoppable if you plant yourself in an environment of growth.

Hydration: Drink half of your body weight in ounces of water each day. If you weigh 150 pounds, divide that by 2, and your water goal will be 75 ounces a day. Keep your water visible and try to finish a few hours before bedtime, otherwise you'll be up all night running to the bathroom.

Nutrition: This one is different for everyone. Think of what your goals are when it comes to what you eat. Your goals might be portion control, cutting out fast food, adding more veggies to your meals, reducing bread, skipping on desserts, giving up soda, or strictly eating clean. We are human, and nothing is ever perfect. Just do your best to stick to your goal.

Sleep: Sleep is essential, but everyone's sleep needs are different. Some people can function well on five to six hours each night while others need more time. Take a couple days to determine what you need. If you wake up refreshed and ready to start the day, you are getting enough sleep. If you are dragging, tired, or cranky, you are most likely not getting enough. Determine how many hours of sleep is your goal and work on getting to bed at a decent time.

Intentional family time: Families don't get strong by chance. It requires engagement, time, and effort. Schedule family time on your calendar, and no matter how many appointments come up, keep your family moments first. This can be uninterrupted one-on-one time or a group date. Some ideas are game night, family bike rides, walks, a trip to the beach, cooking dinner together, or camping out in the yard. Chats are always nice at the end of the day with each one of your kids. Spend some time sharing and being involved.

Random acts of kindness: Every day is an opportunity to be kind. Use Post-it Notes to leave encouraging words for strangers, help someone who is struggling, pay for someone's coffee, compliment someone, leave a note inside a book for someone to find, hold the door open for someone behind you, smile at a stranger, help someone carry their bags, give up your seat, or send a loved one flowers. Being kind can go a long way and improve your emotional well being. It can reduce stress levels, increase your love hormone, and help you connect with people. One small act of kindness can snowball into something much bigger.

REFLECTION

Sorting through your feelings and actions will make it easier to track your progress. It's not always going to be pretty, but being open and honest will help you see just how far you've come. Journaling today means you can go back in 5 years, 10 years, and 20 years and see your hopes, dreams, and struggles. It allows you to see a past version of yourself and all the growth you have experienced. It's so inspiring to go back and see who you were and where you've been.

The following questions are to help you reflect and make adjustments for the next day. Things don't always go as planned, but you are one step ahead by being mindful, tracking, and reviewing.

- **What was your greatest win of the day?**

    Maybe your greatest win is that you completed your workout after contemplating all morning, that you hit your water goal, or that you went out of your way to be kind and it made your day that much better.

- **What changes can you implement to make tomorrow better?**

    Setting out your workout clothes to make it excuse proof, doing your most difficult tasks first thing in the morning, planning ahead on your meals, or getting to bed earlier.

- **My random acts of kindness:**

    What did you do to make someone's day better? How did it make you feel? And start thinking about what you can do tomorrow to shower someone with a bit of sunshine.

- **My one-sentence takeaway from today's reading:**

    There's always a quote or a couple of sentences that inspire us when we read. What jumped out at you that you'd like to go back and read on the days that you struggle?

- **Three things that happened today that I am thankful for:**

    There's always something if we look for it. Our family, running water, a roof over our heads, the ability to move our bodies, people we love, a stranger lending a helping hand, a kind person at the grocery store, teachers, medical staff, our job, and our family's health and safety.

It's okay to struggle because it gives us a chance to be human. The struggle teaches us strength, patience, and humility. Doing the hard things reminds us that we are resilient and makes us feel empowered. You can get through embarrassment, rejection, failure, and heartache. You've done it so many times before, and you are still here to talk about it. This journal is not intended to be unicorns and rainbows every day. You are going to have good days and bad days, but this section is all about keeping it positive and pointing out the good things. You can't change the past, but you can change your tomorrows and make them better.

"Strength doesn't come from what you can do.
It comes from overcoming the things you thought you couldn't."
—Rikki Rogers

M / T / W / T / F / S / S

_____/_____/_____

"Don't figure out the whole race. Just figure out where to put your foot for the starting line. Just start."
—*Jeff Olson*

- ◆ Movement   1   2   3   4   5
- ◆ Read 10 pages   1   2   3   4   5
- ◆ Hydration   1   2   3   4   5
- ◆ Nutrition   1   2   3   4   5
- ◆ Sleep   1   2   3   4   5
- ◆ Intentional family time   1   2   3   4   5
- ◆ Random act of kindness   1   2   3   4   5

What was my greatest win of the day?_____

_____

_____

_____

What changes can I implement to make tomorrow better?

- ◆ _____
- ◆ _____
- ◆ _____

My random act of kindness: _____

_____

_____

My one-sentence takeaway from today's reading: _____

_____

Three things that happened today that I am grateful for:

- ◆ _____
- ◆ _____
- ◆ _____

M / T / W / T / F / S / S

_____/_____/_____

- Movement   1   2   3   4   5
- Read 10 pages   1   2   3   4   5
- Hydration   1   2   3   4   5
- Nutrition   1   2   3   4   5
- Sleep   1   2   3   4   5
- Intentional family time   1   2   3   4   5
- Random act of kindness   1   2   3   4   5

What was my greatest win of the day?_____

_____

_____

_____

What changes can I implement to make tomorrow better?

- _____
- _____
- _____

My random act of kindness: _____

_____

_____

My one-sentence takeaway from today's reading: _____

_____

Three things that happened today that I am grateful for:

- _____
- _____
- _____

M / T / W / T / F / S / S

_____/_____/_____

"Too often we underestimate the power of touch, a smile, a kind word, a listening ear, an honest compliment, or the smallest act of caring, all of which have the potential to turn a life around."
—*Leo Buscaglia*

◆ Movement	1	2	3	4	5
◆ Read 10 pages	1	2	3	4	5
◆ Hydration	1	2	3	4	5
◆ Nutrition	1	2	3	4	5
◆ Sleep	1	2	3	4	5
◆ Intentional family time	1	2	3	4	5
◆ Random act of kindness	1	2	3	4	5

What was my greatest win of the day? _____
_____
_____
_____

What changes can I implement to make tomorrow better?

◆ _____

◆ _____

◆ _____

My random act of kindness: _____
_____
_____

My one-sentence takeaway from today's reading: _____
_____

Three things that happened today that I am grateful for:

◆ _____

◆ _____

◆ _____

M / T / W / T / F / S / S

_____/_____/_____

- ◆ Movement   1   2   3   4   5
- ◆ Read 10 pages   1   2   3   4   5
- ◆ Hydration   1   2   3   4   5
- ◆ Nutrition   1   2   3   4   5
- ◆ Sleep   1   2   3   4   5
- ◆ Intentional family time   1   2   3   4   5
- ◆ Random act of kindness   1   2   3   4   5

What was my greatest win of the day?_____

_____

_____

_____

What changes can I implement to make tomorrow better?

- ◆ _____
- ◆ _____
- ◆ _____

My random act of kindness: _____

_____

_____

My one-sentence takeaway from today's reading: _____

_____

Three things that happened today that I am grateful for:

- ◆ _____
- ◆ _____
- ◆ _____

M / T / W / T / F / S / S

_____/_____/_____

- ◆ Movement   1   2   3   4   5
- ◆ Read 10 pages   1   2   3   4   5
- ◆ Hydration   1   2   3   4   5
- ◆ Nutrition   1   2   3   4   5
- ◆ Sleep   1   2   3   4   5
- ◆ Intentional family time   1   2   3   4   5
- ◆ Random act of kindness   1   2   3   4   5

What was my greatest win of the day?_____

_____

_____

_____

What changes can I implement to make tomorrow better?

- ◆ _____

- ◆ _____

- ◆ _____

My random act of kindness: _____

_____

_____

My one-sentence takeaway from today's reading: _____

_____

Three things that happened today that I am grateful for:

- ◆ _____

- ◆ _____

- ◆ _____

M / T / W / T / F / S / S

_____/_____/_____

- ◆ Movement   1   2   3   4   5
- ◆ Read 10 pages   1   2   3   4   5
- ◆ Hydration   1   2   3   4   5
- ◆ Nutrition   1   2   3   4   5
- ◆ Sleep   1   2   3   4   5
- ◆ Intentional family time   1   2   3   4   5
- ◆ Random act of kindness   1   2   3   4   5

What was my greatest win of the day?_____

_____

_____

_____

What changes can I implement to make tomorrow better?

- ◆ _____
- ◆ _____
- ◆ _____

My random act of kindness: _____

_____

_____

My one-sentence takeaway from today's reading: _____

_____

Three things that happened today that I am grateful for:

- ◆ _____
- ◆ _____
- ◆ _____

M / T / W / T / F / S / S

"The key is not to prioritize our schedule but to schedule our priorities."
—Stephen Covey

_____/_____/_____

◆ Movement	1	2	3	4	5
◆ Read 10 pages	1	2	3	4	5
◆ Hydration	1	2	3	4	5
◆ Nutrition	1	2	3	4	5
◆ Sleep	1	2	3	4	5
◆ Intentional family time	1	2	3	4	5
◆ Random act of kindness	1	2	3	4	5

What was my greatest win of the day?_____

_____

_____

_____

What changes can I implement to make tomorrow better?

◆ _____

◆ _____

◆ _____

My random act of kindness: _____

_____

_____

My one-sentence takeaway from today's reading: _____

_____

Three things that happened today that I am grateful for:

◆ _____

◆ _____

◆ _____

YOUR SPEED DOESN'T MATTER

I used to have an all-or-nothing mentality. Either I was strictly committed and focused, or I gave up all together. I was extreme on both ends and stuck in the "I'll just start Monday" cycle whenever I stumbled. I thought I had to be 100 percent perfect, and if I couldn't deliver, I felt like I was failing.

The problem is that I was missing all the good stuff in the middle. I was missing the little steps I could have climbed if only I kept going despite my slipup. I was missing the learning lessons about what I could do differently to help my progress, and I was missing the opportunity to redefine what's truly important.

You are going to have days where nothing goes right. Some days will be harder than others, but you can't let the little mistakes get in the way of your bigger goal. Understand that we are human, and we are going to have moments where we completely fall off. Work on making better decisions in the moments that follow. Don't waste the entire day because of one bad choice.

We can develop healthier habits and behaviors that will help us long-term. We don't have to be perfect. We can take our time to get there and make sure that it's a sustainable way of living. Your speed doesn't matter: Forward is forward.

- On the days you are feeling discouraged: Fuel your mind. Read a good book on motivation or listen to an inspiring podcast.

- On the days that you don't feel like working out: Reach out for support and get some movement in even if it's only a 10-minute walk.

- On the days that you are feeling tired: Avoid eating foods that make you feel sluggish. Instead fuel your body with foods that are going to give you more energy. Be cautious of what you are putting into your body.

- On the days that you are feeling sad: Surround yourself with people who inspire you and remind you how amazing you are.

- On the days you are feeling stuck: Be brave! Jump out of your comfort zone. We grow the most when we are uncomfortable or scared and when we are trying new things.

Remember: You have done difficult thing in your past. The challenge you are facing now requires the same amount of effort. It's only a different mountain. It really doesn't matter how slow you go, as long as you keep moving. Life is not a sprint; it's a marathon. Take your time and run this race slow and steady.

M / T / W / T / F / S / S

"Exercise is a celebration of what the body can do, not a punishment for what you ate."
—Unknown

_____/_____/_____

	1	2	3	4	5
◆ Movement	1	2	3	4	5
◆ Read 10 pages	1	2	3	4	5
◆ Hydration	1	2	3	4	5
◆ Nutrition	1	2	3	4	5
◆ Sleep	1	2	3	4	5
◆ Intentional family time	1	2	3	4	5
◆ Random act of kindness	1	2	3	4	5

What was my greatest win of the day?_____

_____

_____

_____

What changes can I implement to make tomorrow better?

◆ _____

◆ _____

◆ _____

My random act of kindness: _____

_____

_____

My one-sentence takeaway from today's reading: _____

_____

Three things that happened today that I am grateful for:

◆ _____

◆ _____

◆ _____

M / T / W / T / F / S / S

_____ / _____ / _____

"When you fall in love with the process rather than the product, you don't have to wait to give yourself permission to be happy. You can be satisfied anytime your system is running."
—*James Clear*

	1	2	3	4	5
◆ Movement	1	2	3	4	5
◆ Read 10 pages	1	2	3	4	5
◆ Hydration	1	2	3	4	5
◆ Nutrition	1	2	3	4	5
◆ Sleep	1	2	3	4	5
◆ Intentional family time	1	2	3	4	5
◆ Random act of kindness	1	2	3	4	5

What was my greatest win of the day? _____
_____
_____
_____

What changes can I implement to make tomorrow better?

◆ _____
◆ _____
◆ _____

My random act of kindness: _____
_____
_____

My one-sentence takeaway from today's reading: _____
_____

Three things that happened today that I am grateful for:

◆ _____
◆ _____
◆ _____

M / T / W / T / F / S / S

_____/_____/_____

- Movement   1   2   3   4   5
- Read 10 pages   1   2   3   4   5
- Hydration   1   2   3   4   5
- Nutrition   1   2   3   4   5
- Sleep   1   2   3   4   5
- Intentional family time   1   2   3   4   5
- Random act of kindness   1   2   3   4   5

What was my greatest win of the day?_____

_____

_____

_____

What changes can I implement to make tomorrow better?

- _____
- _____
- _____

My random act of kindness: _____

_____

_____

My one-sentence takeaway from today's reading: _____

_____

Three things that happened today that I am grateful for:

- _____
- _____
- _____

M / T / W / T / F / S / S

_____/_____/_____

◆ Movement	1	2	3	4	5
◆ Read 10 pages	1	2	3	4	5
◆ Hydration	1	2	3	4	5
◆ Nutrition	1	2	3	4	5
◆ Sleep	1	2	3	4	5
◆ Intentional family time	1	2	3	4	5
◆ Random act of kindness	1	2	3	4	5

What was my greatest win of the day?_____

_____

_____

_____

What changes can I implement to make tomorrow better?

◆ _____

◆ _____

◆ _____

My random act of kindness: _____

_____

_____

My one-sentence takeaway from today's reading: _____

_____

Three things that happened today that I am grateful for:

◆ _____

◆ _____

◆ _____

M / T / W / T / F / S / S

_____ / _____ / _____

- ◆ Movement   1   2   3   4   5
- ◆ Read 10 pages   1   2   3   4   5
- ◆ Hydration   1   2   3   4   5
- ◆ Nutrition   1   2   3   4   5
- ◆ Sleep   1   2   3   4   5
- ◆ Intentional family time   1   2   3   4   5
- ◆ Random act of kindness   1   2   3   4   5

What was my greatest win of the day? _____

_____

_____

_____

What changes can I implement to make tomorrow better?

- ◆ _____
- ◆ _____
- ◆ _____

My random act of kindness: _____

_____

_____

My one-sentence takeaway from today's reading: _____

_____

Three things that happened today that I am grateful for:

- ◆ _____
- ◆ _____
- ◆ _____

M / T / W / T / F / S / S

_____ / _____ / _____

	1	2	3	4	5
◆ Movement	1	2	3	4	5
◆ Read 10 pages	1	2	3	4	5
◆ Hydration	1	2	3	4	5
◆ Nutrition	1	2	3	4	5
◆ Sleep	1	2	3	4	5
◆ Intentional family time	1	2	3	4	5
◆ Random act of kindness	1	2	3	4	5

What was my greatest win of the day? _____

_____

_____

_____

What changes can I implement to make tomorrow better?

◆ _____

◆ _____

◆ _____

My random act of kindness: _____

_____

_____

My one-sentence takeaway from today's reading: _____

_____

Three things that happened today that I am grateful for:

◆ _____

◆ _____

◆ _____

M / T / W / T / F / S / S

_____/_____/_____

"Birds fly together because they are headed in the same direction. Ask yourself if your flock is traveling where you want to be headed."
—Unknown

- Movement   1   2   3   4   5
- Read 10 pages   1   2   3   4   5
- Hydration   1   2   3   4   5
- Nutrition   1   2   3   4   5
- Sleep   1   2   3   4   5
- Intentional family time   1   2   3   4   5
- Random act of kindness   1   2   3   4   5

What was my greatest win of the day?_____

_____

_____

_____

What changes can I implement to make tomorrow better?

- _____
- _____
- _____

My random act of kindness: _____

_____

_____

My one-sentence takeaway from today's reading: _____

_____

Three things that happened today that I am grateful for:

- _____
- _____
- _____

NUTRITION, BALANCE, AND MODERATION

At the end of a long workday, all I ever wanted was to treat myself, and that always came in the form of food. I couldn't wait to get home and start my evening routine in front of the TV with a giant bowl of ice cream.

We tend to eat badly when we are busy, stressed, or upset because we think it will make us feel better, when in reality it sucks what little energy we have left. We are what we eat, and feeling tired, sluggish, and depressed made me realize that I wasn't being smart about my meal choices. I had to stop those bad habits and work on my relationship with food. It wasn't just about losing weight to wear smaller jeans. It was more about making myself feel better internally and setting the best example for my kids.

Good health can also be inherited, but we must play an active role in teaching our kids how to properly fuel their bodies. The human body is an amazing machine, and it needs fuel to function at its best. When we eat healthier meals, it helps every aspect of our life. You'll be amazed at how beneficial it is in your work life, family, and marriage.

These tips will help you save time and energy so that eating healthier will be much easier for you and your family. Try to incorporate some of these small changes to work on your nutrition.

- Our body needs the five food groups. Carbohydrates have a negative reputation because so many people reach for the wrong ones. Forget about thinking you have to give up carbohydrates. Eat grains, especially whole grains like whole wheat pasta, whole wheat bread, brown rice, oats, and quinoa.

- Protein increases muscle mass, lowers your blood pressure, and helps repair tissue. Eat foods that are high in protein, such as eggs, chicken, lean turkey, fish, Greek yogurt, cottage cheese, and almonds.

- Fruits and veggies are great sources of vitamins and minerals. They are easier for your body to digest and satisfy sugar cravings. Chop fruits and veggies and put 1 cup servings into Ziploc bags for an easier, already prepared snack.

- You might think that your bones are already hard and don't change once you stop growing, but they are constantly rebuilding. Yogurt, milk, salmon, tuna, dark leafy greens, and almond butter are just some of the many foods that can help make your bones stronger.

- Go through your fridge/pantry and replace junk food with healthier options. Crazy schedules and eating on the run can lead to unhealthy choices.

- Don't eat in front of the TV. This will trick your mind into wanting a snack every time you are watching a show. Make a habit out of having dinner at the table with your family. Sadly, many people don't do this enough.

- Don't go grocery shopping when you are hungry. The things I bring home on an empty stomach are usually not on my grocery list.

- Meal prepping on Sunday will save you time and money during the week. It takes a little longer, but it pays off in the long run.

- Kids are going to eat what you buy. If you don't want them eating chips, cupcakes, and sodas, don't buy them. Fill up your fruit basket and make it visible.

- Take your kids grocery shopping with you and let them pick the fruits for the week. They'll be more excited to eat something if they think it was their idea.

- Don't eat out of a package. It's much more difficult to overeat when you don't have the bag in front of you.

- Try eating smaller portions. Sometimes a few bites of something can fulfill a sugar urge.

- Eat slowly and enjoy your meal. Doing this sends a signal to your brain that you are starting to get full, and it prevents overeating.

- Try to replace juice and soda with water to cut back on sugar intake.

Mental health is just as important as physical health. Don't stress out by depriving yourself of treats that you love. That will set you up for failure, and you will eventually binge. We should strive for a positive and peaceful relationship with food. At a celebration, enjoy a small piece of cake. During a movie, share some popcorn. On a hot summer day, have a scoop of ice cream. It's not what we do once in a while; it's what we do every day that matters most. Find a happy balance.

"Nutrition is king, exercise is queen, put them together and you've got a kingdom."
—Unknown

M / T / W / T / F / S / S

_____/_____/_____

- ◆ Movement   1   2   3   4   5
- ◆ Read 10 pages   1   2   3   4   5
- ◆ Hydration   1   2   3   4   5
- ◆ Nutrition   1   2   3   4   5
- ◆ Sleep   1   2   3   4   5
- ◆ Intentional family time   1   2   3   4   5
- ◆ Random act of kindness   1   2   3   4   5

What was my greatest win of the day?_____

_____

_____

_____

What changes can I implement to make tomorrow better?

- ◆ _____

- ◆ _____

- ◆ _____

My random act of kindness: _____

_____

_____

My one-sentence takeaway from today's reading: _____

_____

Three things that happened today that I am grateful for:

- ◆ _____

- ◆ _____

- ◆ _____

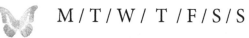

M / T / W / T / F / S / S

"It's not whether you get knocked down;
it's whether you get back up."
—Vince Lombardi

_____/_____/_____

◆ Movement	1	2	3	4	5
◆ Read 10 pages	1	2	3	4	5
◆ Hydration	1	2	3	4	5
◆ Nutrition	1	2	3	4	5
◆ Sleep	1	2	3	4	5
◆ Intentional family time	1	2	3	4	5
◆ Random act of kindness	1	2	3	4	5

What was my greatest win of the day?_____

_____

_____

_____

What changes can I implement to make tomorrow better?

◆ _____

◆ _____

◆ _____

My random act of kindness: _____

_____

_____

My one-sentence takeaway from today's reading: _____

_____

Three things that happened today that I am grateful for:

◆ _____

◆ _____

◆ _____

M / T / W / T / F / S / S

_____/_____/_____

	1	2	3	4	5
◆ Movement	1	2	3	4	5
◆ Read 10 pages	1	2	3	4	5
◆ Hydration	1	2	3	4	5
◆ Nutrition	1	2	3	4	5
◆ Sleep	1	2	3	4	5
◆ Intentional family time	1	2	3	4	5
◆ Random act of kindness	1	2	3	4	5

What was my greatest win of the day?_____

_____

_____

_____

What changes can I implement to make tomorrow better?

◆ _____

◆ _____

◆ _____

My random act of kindness: _____

_____

_____

My one-sentence takeaway from today's reading: _____

_____

Three things that happened today that I am grateful for:

◆ _____

◆ _____

◆ _____

M / T / W / T / F / S / S

"There is a natural progression to everything in life:
Plant, cultivate, and harvest."
—Jeff Olson

_____/_____/_____

◆ Movement	1	2	3	4	5
◆ Read 10 pages	1	2	3	4	5
◆ Hydration	1	2	3	4	5
◆ Nutrition	1	2	3	4	5
◆ Sleep	1	2	3	4	5
◆ Intentional family time	1	2	3	4	5
◆ Random act of kindness	1	2	3	4	5

What was my greatest win of the day?_____

_____

_____

_____

What changes can I implement to make tomorrow better?

◆ _____

◆ _____

◆ _____

My random act of kindness: _____

_____

_____

My one-sentence takeaway from today's reading: _____

_____

Three things that happened today that I am grateful for:

◆ _____

◆ _____

◆ _____

 M / T / W / T / F / S / S

_____/_____/_____

◆ Movement	1	2	3	4	5
◆ Read 10 pages	1	2	3	4	5
◆ Hydration	1	2	3	4	5
◆ Nutrition	1	2	3	4	5
◆ Sleep	1	2	3	4	5
◆ Intentional family time	1	2	3	4	5
◆ Random act of kindness	1	2	3	4	5

What was my greatest win of the day?_____

_____

_____

_____

What changes can I implement to make tomorrow better?

◆ _____

◆ _____

◆ _____

My random act of kindness: _____

_____

_____

My one-sentence takeaway from today's reading: _____

_____

Three things that happened today that I am grateful for:

◆ _____

◆ _____

◆ _____

M / T / W / T / F / S / S

_____/_____/_____

- ◆ Movement   1   2   3   4   5
- ◆ Read 10 pages   1   2   3   4   5
- ◆ Hydration   1   2   3   4   5
- ◆ Nutrition   1   2   3   4   5
- ◆ Sleep   1   2   3   4   5
- ◆ Intentional family time   1   2   3   4   5
- ◆ Random act of kindness   1   2   3   4   5

What was my greatest win of the day?_____

_____

_____

_____

What changes can I implement to make tomorrow better?

- ◆ _____
- ◆ _____
- ◆ _____

My random act of kindness: _____

_____

_____

My one-sentence takeaway from today's reading: _____

_____

Three things that happened today that I am grateful for:

- ◆ _____
- ◆ _____
- ◆ _____

M / T / W / T / F / S / S

_____/_____/_____

- Movement   1   2   3   4   5
- Read 10 pages   1   2   3   4   5
- Hydration   1   2   3   4   5
- Nutrition   1   2   3   4   5
- Sleep   1   2   3   4   5
- Intentional family time   1   2   3   4   5
- Random act of kindness   1   2   3   4   5

What was my greatest win of the day?_____

_____

_____

_____

What changes can I implement to make tomorrow better?

- _____

- _____

- _____

My random act of kindness: _____

_____

_____

My one-sentence takeaway from today's reading: _____

_____

Three things that happened today that I am grateful for:

- _____

- _____

- _____

WHAT WILL PEOPLE SAY?!

This might not be your circumstance, but it was mine for a lot of years. I was always looking for the approval of others to fill a cup that only I could fill. I grew up being more concerned about how others viewed me than how I viewed myself. I assumed what everyone thought about me, not realizing that it was my own beliefs and all I was doing was shifting the blame to someone else. Sadly, this stopped me from growing and jumping into new opportunities.

When other people extend their support, it lights a fire in us that helps us continue with the climb. It's an amazing feeling to know that we are valued, appreciated, and supported. On our journey to happiness, there will also be people who will throw stones our way. Understand that their judgment is not about you, but rather it's more about them. The truth is: People are always going to have an opinion, and we shouldn't take it personally. All that matters is that we are happy and supported by those we love. Seek guidance and advice from those people you do value. Nobody has the right to judge you when you have crawled your way out and worked tirelessly to become who you are today.

I stopped worrying about other people's opinions when I discovered a deeper and stronger sense of who I really am. This required more effort, but it pushed me to live my life with more purpose. It truly is about making a difference and climbing up the mountain together. When we challenge ourselves and step out of our comfort zone, we discover some of our greatest strengths. Be the bigger person, keep chasing your dreams, let go of the past, learn from your mistakes, and keep going no matter what anyone has to say.

If you know someone who is working hard on becoming a better version of themselves, encourage them. Don't be a roadblock on their journey. Instead, help clear the way so that their path is a little less bumpy.

"If you judge people, you have no time to love them."
—Mother Teresa

M / T / W / T / F / S / S

"Be the change that you wish to see in the world."
—Mahatma Gandhi

_____/_____/_____

◆ Movement	1	2	3	4	5
◆ Read 10 pages	1	2	3	4	5
◆ Hydration	1	2	3	4	5
◆ Nutrition	1	2	3	4	5
◆ Sleep	1	2	3	4	5
◆ Intentional family time	1	2	3	4	5
◆ Random act of kindness	1	2	3	4	5

What was my greatest win of the day?_____

_____

_____

_____

What changes can I implement to make tomorrow better?

◆ _____

◆ _____

◆ _____

My random act of kindness: _____

_____

_____

My one-sentence takeaway from today's reading: _____

_____

Three things that happened today that I am grateful for:

◆ _____

◆ _____

◆ _____

M / T / W / T / F / S / S

_____/_____/_____

◆ Movement	1	2	3	4	5
◆ Read 10 pages	1	2	3	4	5
◆ Hydration	1	2	3	4	5
◆ Nutrition	1	2	3	4	5
◆ Sleep	1	2	3	4	5
◆ Intentional family time	1	2	3	4	5
◆ Random act of kindness	1	2	3	4	5

What was my greatest win of the day?_____

_____

_____

_____

What changes can I implement to make tomorrow better?

◆ _____

◆ _____

◆ _____

My random act of kindness: _____

_____

_____

My one-sentence takeaway from today's reading: _____

_____

Three things that happened today that I am grateful for:

◆ _____

◆ _____

◆ _____

M / T / W / T / F / S / S

_____ / _____ / _____

"You can't do anything about the length of your life, but you can do something about its width and depth."
—Evan Esar

◆ Movement	1	2	3	4	5
◆ Read 10 pages	1	2	3	4	5
◆ Hydration	1	2	3	4	5
◆ Nutrition	1	2	3	4	5
◆ Sleep	1	2	3	4	5
◆ Intentional family time	1	2	3	4	5
◆ Random act of kindness	1	2	3	4	5

What was my greatest win of the day? _____

_____

_____

_____

What changes can I implement to make tomorrow better?

◆ _____

◆ _____

◆ _____

My random act of kindness: _____

_____

_____

My one-sentence takeaway from today's reading: _____

_____

Three things that happened today that I am grateful for:

◆ _____

◆ _____

◆ _____

M / T / W / T / F / S / S

"Never look down on anybody unless you're helping them up."
—*Jesse Jackson*

_____/_____/_____

◆ Movement	1	2	3	4	5
◆ Read 10 pages	1	2	3	4	5
◆ Hydration	1	2	3	4	5
◆ Nutrition	1	2	3	4	5
◆ Sleep	1	2	3	4	5
◆ Intentional family time	1	2	3	4	5
◆ Random act of kindness	1	2	3	4	5

What was my greatest win of the day?_____

_____

_____

_____

What changes can I implement to make tomorrow better?

◆ _____

◆ _____

◆ _____

My random act of kindness: _____

_____

_____

My one-sentence takeaway from today's reading: _____

_____

Three things that happened today that I am grateful for:

◆ _____

◆ _____

◆ _____

 M / T / W / T / F / S / S

_____/_____/_____

"A single act of kindness throws out roots in all directions, and the roots spring up and make trees."
—Amelia Earhart

- ◆ Movement   1   2   3   4   5
- ◆ Read 10 pages   1   2   3   4   5
- ◆ Hydration   1   2   3   4   5
- ◆ Nutrition   1   2   3   4   5
- ◆ Sleep   1   2   3   4   5
- ◆ Intentional family time   1   2   3   4   5
- ◆ Random act of kindness   1   2   3   4   5

What was my greatest win of the day?_____

_____

_____

_____

What changes can I implement to make tomorrow better?

- ◆ _____
- ◆ _____
- ◆ _____

My random act of kindness: _____

_____

_____

My one-sentence takeaway from today's reading: _____

_____

Three things that happened today that I am grateful for:

- ◆ _____
- ◆ _____
- ◆ _____

 M / T / W / T / F / S / S

_____ / _____ / _____

"Compassion isn't about solutions.
It's about giving all the love that you've got."
—Cheryl Strayed

- ◆ Movement   1   2   3   4   5
- ◆ Read 10 pages   1   2   3   4   5
- ◆ Hydration   1   2   3   4   5
- ◆ Nutrition   1   2   3   4   5
- ◆ Sleep   1   2   3   4   5
- ◆ Intentional family time   1   2   3   4   5
- ◆ Random act of kindness   1   2   3   4   5

What was my greatest win of the day?_____

_____

_____

_____

What changes can I implement to make tomorrow better?

- ◆ _____
- ◆ _____
- ◆ _____

My random act of kindness: _____

_____

_____

My one-sentence takeaway from today's reading: _____

_____

Three things that happened today that I am grateful for:

- ◆ _____
- ◆ _____
- ◆ _____

M / T / W / T / F / S / S

_____/_____/_____

◆ Movement	1	2	3	4	5
◆ Read 10 pages	1	2	3	4	5
◆ Hydration	1	2	3	4	5
◆ Nutrition	1	2	3	4	5
◆ Sleep	1	2	3	4	5
◆ Intentional family time	1	2	3	4	5
◆ Random act of kindness	1	2	3	4	5

What was my greatest win of the day?_____

_____

_____

_____

What changes can I implement to make tomorrow better?

◆ _____

◆ _____

◆ _____

My random act of kindness: _____

_____

_____

My one-sentence takeaway from today's reading: _____

_____

Three things that happened today that I am grateful for:

◆ _____

◆ _____

◆ _____

SHINE BRIGHT

Like most people, I have really good days and really hard days. I keep glow sticks in random places as a reminder for the hard days. In order for a glow stick to work as it is intended, to provide the glow, it has to be snapped. You have to break it in order to activate the chemicals, and the more you shake it, the more intense it glows.

It took me multiple breaks before I found the power to shine. It wasn't as easy as shaking the tube to make the two chemicals react. I had to work hard, stop feeling guilty about making time for myself, and stick to a consistent routine. Doing that is the only way that we can shine bright and light the path for others.

Of course, the glow won't last forever. Neither will our habits and routines. Things are always changing. We go through loss, we hurt, we get sick, and we feel lost and unmotivated. The important thing to remember is that every morning we are given the opportunity to shine. Whenever you are going through a storm, remember that you have to break in order to shine. When you are in a dark place, reflect upon the things you were doing that made you feel at your very best and get back to doing them.

It might feel strange when we finally step into a new light—almost as if it were impossible to change and evolve from the person you once were, but the bright light is proof that you are becoming who you were meant to be. You will start to feel more comfortable in your own skin when you embrace the changes and shine without holding back. Shine your light and help give others the ability to find theirs.

Part of shining bright is sharing the light and supporting those around us. As James Keller said, "A candle loses nothing by lighting another candle." This world is big enough for us all, and giving extra support will not take away from us. In fact, it adds more to our life. Helping others on their journey fulfills some of our human needs. It helps us connect with others and see our actions make a positive difference. We can always turn on the light.

"Don't be afraid to shine. The world needs your light."
—Timi Nadela

 M / T / W / T / F / S / S

"It's not enough to have lived.
We should be determined to live for something."
—Winston Churchill

_____/_____/_____

◆ Movement	1	2	3	4	5
◆ Read 10 pages	1	2	3	4	5
◆ Hydration	1	2	3	4	5
◆ Nutrition	1	2	3	4	5
◆ Sleep	1	2	3	4	5
◆ Intentional family time	1	2	3	4	5
◆ Random act of kindness	1	2	3	4	5

What was my greatest win of the day?_____

_____

_____

_____

What changes can I implement to make tomorrow better?

◆ _____

◆ _____

◆ _____

My random act of kindness: _____

_____

_____

My one-sentence takeaway from today's reading: _____

_____

Three things that happened today that I am grateful for:

◆ _____

◆ _____

◆ _____

M / T / W / T / F / S / S

"If you do what you've always done,
you'll get what you've always gotten."
—*Tony Robbins*

_____/_____/_____

◆ Movement	1	2	3	4	5
◆ Read 10 pages	1	2	3	4	5
◆ Hydration	1	2	3	4	5
◆ Nutrition	1	2	3	4	5
◆ Sleep	1	2	3	4	5
◆ Intentional family time	1	2	3	4	5
◆ Random act of kindness	1	2	3	4	5

What was my greatest win of the day?_____

_____

_____

_____

What changes can I implement to make tomorrow better?

◆ _____

◆ _____

◆ _____

My random act of kindness: _____

_____

_____

My one-sentence takeaway from today's reading: _____

_____

Three things that happened today that I am grateful for:

◆ _____

◆ _____

◆ _____

 M / T / W / T / F / S / S

"Do the best you can until you know better.
Then when you know better, do better."
—Maya Angelou

_____ / _____ / _____

◆ Movement	1	2	3	4	5
◆ Read 10 pages	1	2	3	4	5
◆ Hydration	1	2	3	4	5
◆ Nutrition	1	2	3	4	5
◆ Sleep	1	2	3	4	5
◆ Intentional family time	1	2	3	4	5
◆ Random act of kindness	1	2	3	4	5

What was my greatest win of the day? _____

_____

_____

_____

What changes can I implement to make tomorrow better?

◆ _____

◆ _____

◆ _____

My random act of kindness: _____

_____

_____

My one-sentence takeaway from today's reading: _____

_____

Three things that happened today that I am grateful for:

◆ _____

◆ _____

◆ _____

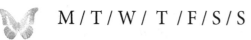 M / T / W / T / F / S / S

"Today I will love myself enough to exercise."
—Unknown

_____/_____/_____

	1	2	3	4	5
◆ Movement	1	2	3	4	5
◆ Read 10 pages	1	2	3	4	5
◆ Hydration	1	2	3	4	5
◆ Nutrition	1	2	3	4	5
◆ Sleep	1	2	3	4	5
◆ Intentional family time	1	2	3	4	5
◆ Random act of kindness	1	2	3	4	5

What was my greatest win of the day?_____

_____

_____

_____

What changes can I implement to make tomorrow better?

◆ _____

◆ _____

◆ _____

My random act of kindness: _____

_____

_____

My one-sentence takeaway from today's reading: _____

_____

Three things that happened today that I am grateful for:

◆ _____

◆ _____

◆ _____

M / T / W / T / F / S / S

_____/_____/_____

"Love and kindness are never wasted. They always make a difference. They bless the one who receives them, and the one who gives."
—Barbara De Angelis

◆ Movement	1	2	3	4	5
◆ Read 10 pages	1	2	3	4	5
◆ Hydration	1	2	3	4	5
◆ Nutrition	1	2	3	4	5
◆ Sleep	1	2	3	4	5
◆ Intentional family time	1	2	3	4	5
◆ Random act of kindness	1	2	3	4	5

What was my greatest win of the day?_____

_____

_____

_____

What changes can I implement to make tomorrow better?

◆ _____

◆ _____

◆ _____

My random act of kindness: _____

_____

_____

My one-sentence takeaway from today's reading: _____

_____

Three things that happened today that I am grateful for:

◆ _____

◆ _____

◆ _____

M / T / W / T / F / S / S

_____/_____/_____

- Movement   1   2   3   4   5
- Read 10 pages   1   2   3   4   5
- Hydration   1   2   3   4   5
- Nutrition   1   2   3   4   5
- Sleep   1   2   3   4   5
- Intentional family time   1   2   3   4   5
- Random act of kindness   1   2   3   4   5

What was my greatest win of the day?_____

_____

_____

_____

What changes can I implement to make tomorrow better?

- _____
- _____
- _____

My random act of kindness: _____

_____

_____

My one-sentence takeaway from today's reading: _____

_____

Three things that happened today that I am grateful for:

- _____
- _____
- _____

M / T / W / T / F / S / S

_____/_____/_____

- ◆ Movement   1   2   3   4   5
- ◆ Read 10 pages   1   2   3   4   5
- ◆ Hydration   1   2   3   4   5
- ◆ Nutrition   1   2   3   4   5
- ◆ Sleep   1   2   3   4   5
- ◆ Intentional family time   1   2   3   4   5
- ◆ Random act of kindness   1   2   3   4   5

What was my greatest win of the day?_____

_____

_____

_____

What changes can I implement to make tomorrow better?

- ◆ _____
- ◆ _____
- ◆ _____

My random act of kindness: _____

_____

_____

My one-sentence takeaway from today's reading: _____

_____

Three things that happened today that I am grateful for:

- ◆ _____
- ◆ _____
- ◆ _____

MOVEMENT

For 15 years, I paid a monthly fee for a gym membership that I rarely used. Feeling motivated and determined, I spent weeks consistently going to the gym. Then life got busy, and one day turned into two, and two days turned into months, making it difficult to find my way back. I needed to find a better system—one that didn't have me convincing myself that it was too far, too much traffic, too crowded, or required a babysitter.

Then I started wondering, if other people could stay consistent and see results, why would I be any different? I finally found a system that I could do at home that worked for me. I needed some direction and signed up with a workout program that gave me access to amazing trainers for a very low cost. I purchased light weights, resistant loops, and sliders. I set up an excuse-proof environment by preparing my clothes and shoes and filling my water bottle the night before.

I woke up every morning and completed a 30-minute workout in my living room. I could do it with crazy hair and not worry about who was watching me struggle.

Except, my kids *were* watching me! They saw me struggle, but they never saw me quit. It became the new normal in our home to pull out the weights and yoga mats every day. Now my kids also each kick off their mornings with a workout.

Movement is one of the most basic functions of the body, and it has been shown to have many health benefits, both physically and mentally. When you sit in front of your computer or television, your spine is compressing.

Make some time every day to get up and move. If you work in an office, set alarms to remind you to get up and stretch every few hours.

- Exercise changes your mood. Physical activity stimulates brain chemicals that can leave you feeling happier and more energized. It decreases stress, anxiety, and depression. Have you met anyone who is in a bad mood after a great workout?! Nobody ever regrets a workout.

- It helps you relax and sleep better. Exercise can help you sleep longer and deeper. I turned myself into a morning person after struggling with insomnia for more than a decade. I now get seven to eight hours of sleep every night.

- Exercise helps with weight loss. It will increase your metabolism rate, which will burn more calories. It also helps you maintain and increase muscle mass and keeps your bones strong.

The most difficult part of my new exercise habit was getting up early to complete my workout. One of the things I did that made a huge difference was refusing to hit snooze. I started leaving my phone on the other side of my bedroom, and when my alarm went off at 4:00 in the morning I had no other choice than to walk across the room to turn it off. Once I was up, I was up!

You don't have to start full force; you just have to start somewhere. Get more steps in, park further from the entrance to stores, go on short walks, take the stairs, do a little stretching in the morning, do a couple crunches before bed, do 10 squats every time you go to use the restroom. Even one squat is better than no squats at all.

"The body will become better at whatever you do, or don't do.
If you don't move, your body will make you better at not moving.
If you move, your body will allow more movement."
—*Ido Portal*

M / T / W / T / F / S / S

"It's kind of fun to do the impossible."
—Walt Disney

_____/_____/_____

◆ Movement	1	2	3	4	5
◆ Read 10 pages	1	2	3	4	5
◆ Hydration	1	2	3	4	5
◆ Nutrition	1	2	3	4	5
◆ Sleep	1	2	3	4	5
◆ Intentional family time	1	2	3	4	5
◆ Random act of kindness	1	2	3	4	5

What was my greatest win of the day?_____

_____

_____

_____

What changes can I implement to make tomorrow better?

◆ _____

◆ _____

◆ _____

My random act of kindness: _____

_____

_____

My one-sentence takeaway from today's reading: _____

_____

Three things that happened today that I am grateful for:

◆ _____

◆ _____

◆ _____

M / T / W / T / F / S / S

_____/_____/_____

◆ Movement	1	2	3	4	5
◆ Read 10 pages	1	2	3	4	5
◆ Hydration	1	2	3	4	5
◆ Nutrition	1	2	3	4	5
◆ Sleep	1	2	3	4	5
◆ Intentional family time	1	2	3	4	5
◆ Random act of kindness	1	2	3	4	5

What was my greatest win of the day?_____

_____

_____

_____

What changes can I implement to make tomorrow better?

◆ _____

◆ _____

◆ _____

My random act of kindness: _____

_____

_____

My one-sentence takeaway from today's reading: _____

_____

Three things that happened today that I am grateful for:

◆ _____

◆ _____

◆ _____

M / T / W / T / F / S / S

"Wrinkles should merely indicate where smiles have been."
—*Mark Twain*

_____/_____/_____

	1	2	3	4	5
◆ Movement	1	2	3	4	5
◆ Read 10 pages	1	2	3	4	5
◆ Hydration	1	2	3	4	5
◆ Nutrition	1	2	3	4	5
◆ Sleep	1	2	3	4	5
◆ Intentional family time	1	2	3	4	5
◆ Random act of kindness	1	2	3	4	5

What was my greatest win of the day?_____

_____

_____

_____

What changes can I implement to make tomorrow better?

◆ _____

◆ _____

◆ _____

My random act of kindness: _____

_____

_____

My one-sentence takeaway from today's reading: _____

_____

Three things that happened today that I am grateful for:

◆ _____

◆ _____

◆ _____

M / T / W / T / F / S / S

___/___/___

"We must embrace pain and burn it
as fuel for our journey."
—Kenji Miyazawa

◆ Movement	1	2	3	4	5
◆ Read 10 pages	1	2	3	4	5
◆ Hydration	1	2	3	4	5
◆ Nutrition	1	2	3	4	5
◆ Sleep	1	2	3	4	5
◆ Intentional family time	1	2	3	4	5
◆ Random act of kindness	1	2	3	4	5

What was my greatest win of the day?_____

_____

_____

_____

What changes can I implement to make tomorrow better?

◆ _____

◆ _____

◆ _____

My random act of kindness: _____

_____

_____

My one-sentence takeaway from today's reading: _____

_____

Three things that happened today that I am grateful for:

◆ _____

◆ _____

◆ _____

M / T / W / T / F / S / S

"All great achievements require time."
—Maya Angelou

_____ / _____ / _____

◆ Movement	1	2	3	4	5
◆ Read 10 pages	1	2	3	4	5
◆ Hydration	1	2	3	4	5
◆ Nutrition	1	2	3	4	5
◆ Sleep	1	2	3	4	5
◆ Intentional family time	1	2	3	4	5
◆ Random act of kindness	1	2	3	4	5

What was my greatest win of the day?_____

_____

_____

_____

What changes can I implement to make tomorrow better?

◆ _____

◆ _____

◆ _____

My random act of kindness: _____

_____

_____

My one-sentence takeaway from today's reading: _____

_____

Three things that happened today that I am grateful for:

◆ _____

◆ _____

◆ _____

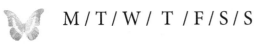

M / T / W / T / F / S / S

_____/_____/_____

"Do things for people not because of who they are or what they do in return, but because of who you are."
—*Harold S. Kushner*

◆ Movement	1	2	3	4	5
◆ Read 10 pages	1	2	3	4	5
◆ Hydration	1	2	3	4	5
◆ Nutrition	1	2	3	4	5
◆ Sleep	1	2	3	4	5
◆ Intentional family time	1	2	3	4	5
◆ Random act of kindness	1	2	3	4	5

What was my greatest win of the day?_____

_____

_____

_____

What changes can I implement to make tomorrow better?

◆ _____

◆ _____

◆ _____

My random act of kindness: _____

_____

_____

My one-sentence takeaway from today's reading: _____

_____

Three things that happened today that I am grateful for:

◆ _____

◆ _____

◆ _____

M / T / W / T / F / S / S

*"I can accept failure; everyone fails at something.
But I can't accept not trying."*
—*Michael Jordan*

_____/_____/_____

◆ Movement	1	2	3	4	5
◆ Read 10 pages	1	2	3	4	5
◆ Hydration	1	2	3	4	5
◆ Nutrition	1	2	3	4	5
◆ Sleep	1	2	3	4	5
◆ Intentional family time	1	2	3	4	5
◆ Random act of kindness	1	2	3	4	5

What was my greatest win of the day?_____

_____

_____

_____

What changes can I implement to make tomorrow better?

◆ _____

◆ _____

◆ _____

My random act of kindness: _____

_____

_____

My one-sentence takeaway from today's reading: _____

_____

Three things that happened today that I am grateful for:

◆ _____

◆ _____

◆ _____

COMFORT ZONE

When kids hear music, they sing and dance. As we get older, we stop doing the things we love because we realize people are watching, judging, or even laughing at us.

When was the last time you were really, really proud of yourself? Think about a time when you did something difficult—even though you struggled, even though you were embarrassed, even though you failed before actually succeeding. When you finished that incredibly difficult task, you felt amazing.

The last time you did something difficult, it required a lot of bravery on your part, but I am willing to bet that in the end, you were so happy you took the leap. Vacation is fun, traveling is fun, but pure happiness comes after pushing your limits and being proud of what you have done.

For years, I told myself that I wasn't good with directions. It's human nature to avoid contradicting ourselves, so we do whatever possible to align our behaviors with our beliefs. That kept me in a familiar zone. Traveling to an entirely new destination alone threw me out of my comfort zone. It was years before I could gather the courage to go to an unfamiliar place. Now every time I feel scared or nervous, I dive into it because I know how amazing it feels when I came back up for air.

We all have different fears and experiences. I can't tell you what will push you out of your comfort zone; only you know that. I can tell you that we all have the ability to stretch and grow to become better versions of ourselves, but oftentimes we don't because we are stuck in our comfort zone. We stay there because we fear failure, loss of control, rejection, or embarrassment. It can be scary because we are always thinking of the worst possible scenario, but the more you step out of your comfort zone, the easier it gets.

Even if you make mistakes and don't get it right the first time, they become learning experiences. Don't let your fear of embarrassment become bigger than your love for being happy. The unfamiliar paths are the ones that take you to the best places.

- Be comfortable with being uncomfortable.
- Start up a conversation with a complete stranger.
- Conquer your fears.

- Try something new.

- Recognize when you start making excuses and go against them.

Challenge yourself in small ways so you can build confidence and jump higher. Don't miss out on opportunities, life experiences, and personal growth. Life is too short to play it safe. Get up and dance!

"A ship is always safe at shore, but that is not what it was built for."
—*Albert Einstein*

M / T / W / T / F / S / S

_____/_____/_____

- ◆ Movement   1   2   3   4   5
- ◆ Read 10 pages   1   2   3   4   5
- ◆ Hydration   1   2   3   4   5
- ◆ Nutrition   1   2   3   4   5
- ◆ Sleep   1   2   3   4   5
- ◆ Intentional family time   1   2   3   4   5
- ◆ Random act of kindness   1   2   3   4   5

What was my greatest win of the day?_____

_____

_____

_____

What changes can I implement to make tomorrow better?

- ◆ _____

- ◆ _____

- ◆ _____

My random act of kindness: _____

_____

_____

My one-sentence takeaway from today's reading: _____

_____

Three things that happened today that I am grateful for:

- ◆ _____

- ◆ _____

- ◆ _____

 M / T / W / T / F / S / S

"Do one thing every day that scares you."
—Eleanor Roosevelt

_____/_____/_____

◆ Movement	1	2	3	4	5
◆ Read 10 pages	1	2	3	4	5
◆ Hydration	1	2	3	4	5
◆ Nutrition	1	2	3	4	5
◆ Sleep	1	2	3	4	5
◆ Intentional family time	1	2	3	4	5
◆ Random act of kindness	1	2	3	4	5

What was my greatest win of the day?_____

_____

_____

_____

What changes can I implement to make tomorrow better?

◆ _____

◆ _____

◆ _____

My random act of kindness: _____

_____

_____

My one-sentence takeaway from today's reading: _____

_____

Three things that happened today that I am grateful for:

◆ _____

◆ _____

◆ _____

M / T / W / T / F / S / S

"Wherever there is a human being, there is an opportunity for kindness."
—Lucius Annaeus Seneca

_____/_____/_____

◆ Movement	1	2	3	4	5
◆ Read 10 pages	1	2	3	4	5
◆ Hydration	1	2	3	4	5
◆ Nutrition	1	2	3	4	5
◆ Sleep	1	2	3	4	5
◆ Intentional family time	1	2	3	4	5
◆ Random act of kindness	1	2	3	4	5

What was my greatest win of the day?_____

_____

_____

_____

What changes can I implement to make tomorrow better?

◆ _____

◆ _____

◆ _____

My random act of kindness: _____

_____

_____

My one-sentence takeaway from today's reading: _____

_____

Three things that happened today that I am grateful for:

◆ _____

◆ _____

◆ _____

M / T / W / T / F / S / S

_____/_____/_____

- ◆ Movement   1   2   3   4   5
- ◆ Read 10 pages   1   2   3   4   5
- ◆ Hydration   1   2   3   4   5
- ◆ Nutrition   1   2   3   4   5
- ◆ Sleep   1   2   3   4   5
- ◆ Intentional family time   1   2   3   4   5
- ◆ Random act of kindness   1   2   3   4   5

What was my greatest win of the day?_____

_____

_____

_____

What changes can I implement to make tomorrow better?

- ◆ _____
- ◆ _____
- ◆ _____

My random act of kindness: _____

_____

_____

My one-sentence takeaway from today's reading: _____

_____

Three things that happened today that I am grateful for:

- ◆ _____
- ◆ _____
- ◆ _____

M / T / W / T / F / S / S

"You can either experience the pain of discipline or the pain of regret. The choice is yours."
—Unknown

_____/_____/_____

◆ Movement	1	2	3	4	5
◆ Read 10 pages	1	2	3	4	5
◆ Hydration	1	2	3	4	5
◆ Nutrition	1	2	3	4	5
◆ Sleep	1	2	3	4	5
◆ Intentional family time	1	2	3	4	5
◆ Random act of kindness	1	2	3	4	5

What was my greatest win of the day?_____

_____

_____

_____

What changes can I implement to make tomorrow better?

◆ _____

◆ _____

◆ _____

My random act of kindness: _____

_____

_____

My one-sentence takeaway from today's reading: _____

_____

Three things that happened today that I am grateful for:

◆ _____

◆ _____

◆ _____

M / T / W / T / F / S / S

_____/_____/_____

◆ Movement	1	2	3	4	5
◆ Read 10 pages	1	2	3	4	5
◆ Hydration	1	2	3	4	5
◆ Nutrition	1	2	3	4	5
◆ Sleep	1	2	3	4	5
◆ Intentional family time	1	2	3	4	5
◆ Random act of kindness	1	2	3	4	5

What was my greatest win of the day?_____
_____
_____
_____

What changes can I implement to make tomorrow better?

◆ _____
◆ _____
◆ _____

My random act of kindness: _____
_____
_____

My one-sentence takeaway from today's reading: _____
_____

Three things that happened today that I am grateful for:

◆ _____
◆ _____
◆ _____

M / T / W / T / F / S / S

_____/_____/_____

- ◆ Movement   1   2   3   4   5
- ◆ Read 10 pages   1   2   3   4   5
- ◆ Hydrate   1   2   3   4   5
- ◆ Nutrition   1   2   3   4   5
- ◆ Sleep   1   2   3   4   5
- ◆ Intentional family time   1   2   3   4   5
- ◆ Random act of kindness   1   2   3   4   5

What was my greatest win of the day?_____

_____

_____

_____

What changes can I implement to make tomorrow better?

- ◆ _____
- ◆ _____
- ◆ _____

My random act of kindness: _____

_____

_____

My one-sentence takeaway from today's reading: _____

_____

Three things that happened today that I am grateful for:

- ◆ _____
- ◆ _____
- ◆ _____

MOMENTUM

When an object is moving and has weight, it has momentum. The same can be said about us when we are staying consistent. Momentum is in just about any activity that involves motion and movement. When you have a lot of momentum, it's going to take some effort to stop. When you have momentum on your side, you can steer it in any direction.

Whenever I've had momentum with my health, I've also had it in my side business. When I've had it in my side business, I've also had it in my personal life. You can steer that momentum any direction you want. It can be contagious in other areas, but you have to take the wheel. You do that by finding the principles that have worked in one area and applying them to other areas in your life.

Start with one small step:

- Make your bed every morning.

- Surround yourself with people who want to see you succeed.

- Stay focused on the goal.

- Push yourself more on the harder days.

- Don't miss more than two days at a time.

- Remember 15 minutes is better than nothing at all.

- Focus on one problem at a time.

- Celebrate your small victories.

The key to building momentum is easy. You just have to keep moving. There's one thing that is more difficult than starting—restarting. On the hard days, do the best you can to keep the momentum going. Even if it wasn't your best workout, get it done anyway. When you fail on your nutrition for lunch, do better at dinner. Choose to be grateful for what you have done right and appreciate the moment you are in. Whatever you do, just keep going.

"Nothing can stop a freight train going full speed,
but a block can prevent it from moving when it's at a standstill."
—James Clear

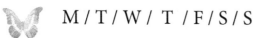

M / T / W / T / F / S / S

"Hold the vision; trust the process."
-Uknown

_____/_____/_____

◆ Movement	1	2	3	4	5
◆ Read 10 pages	1	2	3	4	5
◆ Hydration	1	2	3	4	5
◆ Nutrition	1	2	3	4	5
◆ Sleep	1	2	3	4	5
◆ Intentional family time	1	2	3	4	5
◆ Random act of kindness	1	2	3	4	5

What was my greatest win of the day?_____

_____

_____

_____

What changes can I implement to make tomorrow better?

◆ _____

◆ _____

◆ _____

My random act of kindness: _____

_____

_____

My one-sentence takeaway from today's reading: _____

_____

Three things that happened today that I am grateful for:

◆ _____

◆ _____

◆ _____

M / T / W / T / F / S / S

_____/_____/_____

- ◆ Movement   1   2   3   4   5
- ◆ Read 10 pages   1   2   3   4   5
- ◆ Hydrate   1   2   3   4   5
- ◆ Nutrition   1   2   3   4   5
- ◆ Sleep   1   2   3   4   5
- ◆ Intentional family time   1   2   3   4   5
- ◆ Random act of kindness   1   2   3   4   5

What was my greatest win of the day?_____

_____

_____

_____

What changes can I implement to make tomorrow better?

- ◆ _____
- ◆ _____
- ◆ _____

My random act of kindness: _____

_____

_____

My one-sentence takeaway from today's reading: _____

_____

Three things that happened today that I am grateful for:

- ◆ _____
- ◆ _____
- ◆ _____

M / T / W / T / F / S / S

_____/_____/_____

- Movement   1   2   3   4   5
- Read 10 pages   1   2   3   4   5
- Hydrate   1   2   3   4   5
- Nutrition   1   2   3   4   5
- Sleep   1   2   3   4   5
- Intentional family time   1   2   3   4   5
- Random act of kindness   1   2   3   4   5

What was my greatest win of the day?_____

_____

_____

_____

What changes can I implement to make tomorrow better?

- _____

- _____

- _____

My random act of kindness: _____

_____

_____

My one-sentence takeaway from today's reading: _____

_____

Three things that happened today that I am grateful for:

- _____

- _____

- _____

M / T / W / T / F / S / S

_____/_____/_____

- ◆ Movement   1   2   3   4   5
- ◆ Read 10 pages   1   2   3   4   5
- ◆ Hydrate   1   2   3   4   5
- ◆ Nutrition   1   2   3   4   5
- ◆ Sleep   1   2   3   4   5
- ◆ Intentional family time   1   2   3   4   5
- ◆ Random act of kindness   1   2   3   4   5

What was my greatest win of the day? _____

_____

_____

_____

What changes can I implement to make tomorrow better?

- ◆ _____
- ◆ _____
- ◆ _____

My random act of kindness: _____

_____

_____

My one-sentence takeaway from today's reading: _____

_____

Three things that happened today that I am grateful for:

- ◆ _____
- ◆ _____
- ◆ _____

M / T / W / T / F / S / S

_____/_____/_____

"You don't need to see the whole staircase.
Just take the first step."
—Martin Luther King Jr.

- ◆ Movement   1   2   3   4   5
- ◆ Read 10 pages   1   2   3   4   5
- ◆ Hydrate   1   2   3   4   5
- ◆ Nutrition   1   2   3   4   5
- ◆ Sleep   1   2   3   4   5
- ◆ Intentional family time   1   2   3   4   5
- ◆ Random act of kindness   1   2   3   4   5

What was my greatest win of the day?_____

_____

_____

_____

What changes can I implement to make tomorrow better?

- ◆ _____
- ◆ _____
- ◆ _____

My random act of kindness: _____

_____

_____

My one-sentence takeaway from today's reading: _____

_____

Three things that happened today that I am grateful for:

- ◆ _____
- ◆ _____
- ◆ _____

M / T / W / T / F / S / S

"Don't say you don't have time. You have the same number of hours per day that were given to Helen Keller, Michelangelo, Mother Teresa, Thomas Jefferson, and Albert Einstein."
—*H. Jackson Brown Jr.*

◆ Movement	1	2	3	4	5
◆ Read 10 pages	1	2	3	4	5
◆ Hydrate	1	2	3	4	5
◆ Nutrition	1	2	3	4	5
◆ Sleep	1	2	3	4	5
◆ Intentional family time	1	2	3	4	5
◆ Random act of kindness	1	2	3	4	5

What was my greatest win of the day?_____

_____

_____

_____

What changes can I implement to make tomorrow better?

◆ _____

◆ _____

◆ _____

My random act of kindness: _____

_____

_____

My one-sentence takeaway from today's reading: _____

_____

Three things that happened today that I am grateful for:

◆ _____

◆ _____

◆ _____

M / T / W / T / F / S / S

"At any given moment, you have the power to say: This is not how this story is going to end."
—*Unknown*

_____/_____/_____

◆ Movement	1	2	3	4	5
◆ Read 10 pages	1	2	3	4	5
◆ Hydrate	1	2	3	4	5
◆ Nutrition	1	2	3	4	5
◆ Sleep	1	2	3	4	5
◆ Intentional family time	1	2	3	4	5
◆ Random act of kindness	1	2	3	4	5

What was my greatest win of the day?_____

_____

_____

_____

What changes can I implement to make tomorrow better?

◆ _____

◆ _____

◆ _____

My random act of kindness: _____

_____

_____

My one-sentence takeaway from today's reading: _____

_____

Three things that happened today that I am grateful for:

◆ _____

◆ _____

◆ _____

THE DAY WE PLANT THE SEED

"The day you plant the seed is not the day you eat the fruit."
—Fabienne Fredrickson

Growing is about trial and error and not expecting instant results. We have to work for it, show up day after day, even on the days we are not feeling it. One day, we will get to harvest the benefits from all the sacrifices we've made. We have to give progress time to grow by staying consistent. You didn't get to where you are overnight. It was months or years of negative emotions, lack of sleep, and not taking care of yourself. In trying to make everyone happy, did you completely neglect *your* needs?

It's easy to forget that things take time. We live in an Amazon Prime world. We track our packages and get bothered when the delivery gets delayed. We watch anxiously as the seconds move when we are microwaving our meals. We get frustrated when our internet is taking seconds to load. We get impatient when we are waiting in line for our coffee. Everything is literally in the palm of our hands as soon as we hit send. It's no surprise that we want to see the scale move after one healthy meal, or we want to feel positive after reading one book.

That's not how growth works. In order to see changes, we have to give it time. Most people give up right before the results come. Don't be most people! It's going to take time and discipline before you can see any changes, but once you see them, there's no stopping you. Be patient. The transformation begins on the inside first.

- Don't make a habit out of weighing yourself often. The number on the scale will fluctuate depending on the day. Muscle weighs more than fat, and water retention can make your weight go up quickly. Monitor your progress by how you feel and how your clothes fit.

- Take "before" pictures. I can't tell you how grateful I am that I have photos to look back on. Before and after pictures show incredible transformations. They are important to show results and progress over time. It's an honest starting point that can help you stay consistent.

- One salad won't make you thinner, just like one slice of pizza won't make you bigger. It's important to remember that what matters most is what you do most of the time. Celebrating a birthday with a slice of cake is not going to kill you. If you have a special event coming, try to do better with the meals leading up to it.

Fruits and veggies take different times to grow. Radishes will grow in 21 days, while the pineapple could take more than two years. Don't compare your growth to others. We all grow and change at different rates.

"Patience is not the ability to wait,
but the ability to keep a good attitude while waiting."
—Joyce Meyer

M / T / W / T / F / S / S

_____/_____/_____

- ◆ Movement   1   2   3   4   5
- ◆ Read 10 pages   1   2   3   4   5
- ◆ Hydrate   1   2   3   4   5
- ◆ Nutrition   1   2   3   4   5
- ◆ Sleep   1   2   3   4   5
- ◆ Intentional family time   1   2   3   4   5
- ◆ Random act of kindness   1   2   3   4   5

What was my greatest win of the day?_____

_____

_____

_____

What changes can I implement to make tomorrow better?

- ◆ _____

- ◆ _____

- ◆ _____

My random act of kindness: _____

_____

_____

My one-sentence takeaway from today's reading: _____

_____

Three things that happened today that I am grateful for:

- ◆ _____

- ◆ _____

- ◆ _____

M / T / W / T / F / S / S

_____/_____/_____

- Movement   1   2   3   4   5
- Read 10 pages   1   2   3   4   5
- Hydrate   1   2   3   4   5
- Nutrition   1   2   3   4   5
- Sleep   1   2   3   4   5
- Intentional family time   1   2   3   4   5
- Random act of kindness   1   2   3   4   5

What was my greatest win of the day?_____

_____

_____

_____

What changes can I implement to make tomorrow better?

- _____
- _____
- _____

My random act of kindness: _____

_____

_____

My one-sentence takeaway from today's reading: _____

_____

Three things that happened today that I am grateful for:

- _____
- _____
- _____

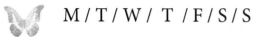

M / T / W / T / F / S / S

_____/_____/_____

	1	2	3	4	5
◆ Movement	1	2	3	4	5
◆ Read 10 pages	1	2	3	4	5
◆ Hydrate	1	2	3	4	5
◆ Nutrition	1	2	3	4	5
◆ Sleep	1	2	3	4	5
◆ Intentional family time	1	2	3	4	5
◆ Random act of kindness	1	2	3	4	5

What was my greatest win of the day?_____

_____

_____

_____

What changes can I implement to make tomorrow better?

◆ _____

◆ _____

◆ _____

My random act of kindness: _____

_____

_____

My one-sentence takeaway from today's reading: _____

_____

Three things that happened today that I am grateful for:

◆ _____

◆ _____

◆ _____

M / T / W / T / F / S / S

_____/_____/_____

- ◆ Movement   1   2   3   4   5
- ◆ Read 10 pages   1   2   3   4   5
- ◆ Hydrate   1   2   3   4   5
- ◆ Nutrition   1   2   3   4   5
- ◆ Sleep   1   2   3   4   5
- ◆ Intentional family time   1   2   3   4   5
- ◆ Random act of kindness   1   2   3   4   5

What was my greatest win of the day?_____

_____

_____

_____

What changes can I implement to make tomorrow better?

- ◆ _____

- ◆ _____

- ◆ _____

My random act of kindness: _____

_____

_____

My one-sentence takeaway from today's reading: _____

_____

Three things that happened today that I am grateful for:

- ◆ _____

- ◆ _____

- ◆ _____

M / T / W / T / F / S / S

"If you can't do anything about it, then let it go.
Don't be a prisoner to things you can't change."
—Tony Gaskins

_____/_____/_____

◆ Movement	1	2	3	4	5
◆ Read 10 pages	1	2	3	4	5
◆ Hydrate	1	2	3	4	5
◆ Nutrition	1	2	3	4	5
◆ Sleep	1	2	3	4	5
◆ Intentional family time	1	2	3	4	5
◆ Random act of kindness	1	2	3	4	5

What was my greatest win of the day?_____

_____

_____

_____

What changes can I implement to make tomorrow better?

◆ _____

◆ _____

◆ _____

My random act of kindness: _____

_____

_____

My one-sentence takeaway from today's reading: _____

_____

Three things that happened today that I am grateful for:

◆ _____

◆ _____

◆ _____

M / T / W / T / F / S / S

"You can't go back and change the beginning,
but you can start where you are and change the ending."
—C.S. Lewis

_____ / _____ / _____

◆ Movement	1	2	3	4	5
◆ Read 10 pages	1	2	3	4	5
◆ Hydrate	1	2	3	4	5
◆ Nutrition	1	2	3	4	5
◆ Sleep	1	2	3	4	5
◆ Intentional family time	1	2	3	4	5
◆ Random act of kindness	1	2	3	4	5

What was my greatest win of the day?_____

_____

_____

_____

What changes can I implement to make tomorrow better?

◆ _____

◆ _____

◆ _____

My random act of kindness: _____

_____

_____

My one-sentence takeaway from today's reading: _____

_____

Three things that happened today that I am grateful for:

◆ _____

◆ _____

◆ _____

M / T / W / T / F / S / S

"I choose to make the rest of my life, the best of my life."
—Louise Hay

_____/_____/_____

◆ Movement	1	2	3	4	5
◆ Read 10 pages	1	2	3	4	5
◆ Hydrate	1	2	3	4	5
◆ Nutrition	1	2	3	4	5
◆ Sleep	1	2	3	4	5
◆ Intentional family time	1	2	3	4	5
◆ Random act of kindness	1	2	3	4	5

What was my greatest win of the day?_____

_____

_____

_____

What changes can I implement to make tomorrow better?

◆ _____

◆ _____

◆ _____

My random act of kindness: _____

_____

_____

My one-sentence takeaway from today's reading: _____

_____

Three things that happened today that I am grateful for:

◆ _____

◆ _____

◆ _____

ADJUST YOUR ENVIRONMENT

Stress is a part of life. You can't always control your circumstances, but you can definitely control how you respond to them. Over the years, I have learned so much about how to make significant changes in my life. The most difficult decision to make turned out to be the one that has brought me the most happiness.

Learning to adjust my environment was life-changing. That meant removing negativity that came my way. Once I started my journey, I realized that I had outgrown my place of work. I finally built up enough courage to move on from my job of 19 years. Before making the decision to leave, I was waking up happy every morning, doing my workout, practicing gratitude, working on my personal development, and taking my happy self to work. My eight-minute drive was peaceful and relaxing because my days were off to a great start. Unfortunately, my happiness didn't last too long.

As soon as I got to work, I was in a negative environment. As much as I tried to fight it, the negativity rubbed off on me. The Zen wife and mom who arrived to work every morning was not the same person who came home at the end of the day. It wasn't fair to my family that I gave my very best to everyone else, and by the time I came home, I was angry and emotionally drained.

It was scary, but I made the decision to leave. From the other side of making that hard decision, I can tell you that sometimes doing scary things takes you to a happier, more fulfilling place.

Here's how to set up your environment to be excuse proof:

- Remove negativity from your life and surround yourself with positive, and inspiring people.
- Remember that just because you've always done things a certain way doesn't mean you can't do things differently.
- Set out your workout clothes and shoes the night before.
- Plan your meals ahead to avoid impulse buying fast food.
- Organize and clean your home every night to wake up in a better mood the next morning.
- Make healthy snacks visible on your kitchen counter. You're more likely to eat them if they are in plain sight.

- Create a calendar on a large white board for your family. Being on the same page with your schedule helps keep the peace at home.

- Fill your bottles with water the night before.

- Do as much as possible in the evenings, rather than waiting until morning. Anything you can do the night before will help your mornings run smoother.

Our environment and relationships are big factors in a healthy, balanced lifestyle. You owe it to yourself to implement habits that will support who you want to be. Set up your environment for success.

M / T / W / T / F / S / S

_____/_____/_____

Yesterday I was clever, so I wanted to change the world. Today I am wise, so I am changing myself."
—*Rumi*

	1	2	3	4	5
◆ Movement	1	2	3	4	5
◆ Read 10 pages	1	2	3	4	5
◆ Hydration	1	2	3	4	5
◆ Nutrition	1	2	3	4	5
◆ Sleep	1	2	3	4	5
◆ Intentional family time	1	2	3	4	5
◆ Random act of kindness	1	2	3	4	5

What was my greatest win of the day?_____

_____

_____

_____

What changes can I implement to make tomorrow better?

◆ _____

◆ _____

◆ _____

My random act of kindness: _____

_____

_____

My one-sentence takeaway from today's reading: _____

_____

Three things that happened today that I am grateful for:

◆ _____

◆ _____

◆ _____

M / T / W / T / F / S / S

"Life moves pretty fast. If you don't stop and look around once in a while, you might miss it."
—Ferris Bueller

_____/_____/_____

◆ Movement	1	2	3	4	5
◆ Read 10 pages	1	2	3	4	5
◆ Hydration	1	2	3	4	5
◆ Nutrition	1	2	3	4	5
◆ Sleep	1	2	3	4	5
◆ Intentional family time	1	2	3	4	5
◆ Random act of kindness	1	2	3	4	5

What was my greatest win of the day?_____

_____

_____

_____

What changes can I implement to make tomorrow better?

◆ _____

◆ _____

◆ _____

My random act of kindness: _____

_____

_____

My one-sentence takeaway from today's reading: _____

_____

Three things that happened today that I am grateful for:

◆ _____

◆ _____

◆ _____

M / T / W / T / F / S / S

_____/_____/_____

*"Love and compassion are necessities, not luxuries.
Without them, humanity cannot survive."*
—Dalai Lama

◆ Movement	1	2	3	4	5
◆ Read 10 pages	1	2	3	4	5
◆ Hydration	1	2	3	4	5
◆ Nutrition	1	2	3	4	5
◆ Sleep	1	2	3	4	5
◆ Intentional family time	1	2	3	4	5
◆ Random act of kindness	1	2	3	4	5

What was my greatest win of the day?_____

_____

_____

_____

What changes can I implement to make tomorrow better?

◆ _____

◆ _____

◆ _____

My random act of kindness: _____

_____

_____

My one-sentence takeaway from today's reading: _____

_____

Three things that happened today that I am grateful for:

◆ _____

◆ _____

◆ _____

M / T / W / T / F / S / S

_____/_____/_____

- ◆ Movement   1   2   3   4   5
- ◆ Read 10 pages   1   2   3   4   5
- ◆ Hydration   1   2   3   4   5
- ◆ Nutrition   1   2   3   4   5
- ◆ Sleep   1   2   3   4   5
- ◆ Intentional family time   1   2   3   4   5
- ◆ Random act of kindness   1   2   3   4   5

What was my greatest win of the day?_____

_____

_____

_____

What changes can I implement to make tomorrow better?

- ◆ _____
- ◆ _____
- ◆ _____

My random act of kindness: _____

_____

_____

My one-sentence takeaway from today's reading: _____

_____

Three things that happened today that I am grateful for:

- ◆ _____
- ◆ _____
- ◆ _____

M / T / W / T / F / S / S

_____/_____/_____

- Movement   1   2   3   4   5
- Read 10 pages   1   2   3   4   5
- Hydration   1   2   3   4   5
- Nutrition   1   2   3   4   5
- Sleep   1   2   3   4   5
- Intentional family time   1   2   3   4   5
- Random act of kindness   1   2   3   4   5

What was my greatest win of the day?_____

_____

_____

_____

What changes can I implement to make tomorrow better?

- _____
- _____
- _____

My random act of kindness: _____

_____

_____

My one-sentence takeaway from today's reading: _____

_____

Three things that happened today that I am grateful for:

- _____
- _____
- _____

M / T / W / T / F / S / S

___/___/_____

- Movement   1   2   3   4   5
- Read 10 pages   1   2   3   4   5
- Hydration   1   2   3   4   5
- Nutrition   1   2   3   4   5
- Sleep   1   2   3   4   5
- Intentional family time   1   2   3   4   5
- Random act of kindness   1   2   3   4   5

What was my greatest win of the day?_____

_____

_____

_____

What changes can I implement to make tomorrow better?

- _____
- _____
- _____

My random act of kindness: _____

_____

_____

My one-sentence takeaway from today's reading: _____

_____

Three things that happened today that I am grateful for:

- _____
- _____
- _____

M / T / W / T / F / S / S

"A diamond is merely a chunk of coal that did well under pressure."
—Unknown

_____ / _____ / _____

	1	2	3	4	5
◆ Movement	1	2	3	4	5
◆ Read 10 pages	1	2	3	4	5
◆ Hydration	1	2	3	4	5
◆ Nutrition	1	2	3	4	5
◆ Sleep	1	2	3	4	5
◆ Intentional family time	1	2	3	4	5
◆ Random act of kindness	1	2	3	4	5

What was my greatest win of the day?_____

_____

_____

_____

What changes can I implement to make tomorrow better?

◆ _____

◆ _____

◆ _____

My random act of kindness: _____

_____

_____

My one-sentence takeaway from today's reading: _____

_____

Three things that happened today that I am grateful for:

◆ _____

◆ _____

◆ _____

CONGRATULATIONS FOR CHOOSING YOURSELF!

I designed this journal to be a 70-day journey—not because it's the perfect amount of days to see significant changes, but because we need deadlines to keep us accountable. Without having a timeframe, we will put things off and procrastinate with the "I'll get there someday" mentality. Urgency creates focus!

Every time we succeed at something, we stop doing the things that got us there. We slowly start changing our eating habits, and soon enough we end up right back where we started. We skip a workout, two workouts, 10 workouts, making it difficult to jump back in. We forget to practice gratitude and work on our personal growth, until one day we notice we are starting to think negatively again.

I don't mean you should never enjoy pizza, ice cream, and cake, or that you should never take a day off. What I am saying is to continue being mindful. Eat in moderation, keep moving your body, and continue to fuel your mind. It's likely been a long 70 days, working tirelessly, giving it everything you have. Continue to do the things that brought you this far, revisit this journal, start a new one, and don't lose all your progress by moving backward.

This is not the end: It's the start of something amazing. You don't get to the finish line and forget everything you learned along the way. Now is the time to continue to implement all these new habits and make them a part of who you are.

You are the greatest project you'll ever work on.
Go and create magic!

ACKNOWLEDGMENTS

Who I am today could not have been possible without the exceptional human beings who I have the privilege of doing life with. My husband of 18 years, Frazier Godinez, who is my biggest supporter: I am so thankful for his love, his calm aura, and his belief in my ability to do things I never imagined.

Thanks to our three children, Alana, Julian, and Leila for their loving support as I navigate this life and for their unfailing patience as I find my place in it. They are the reason I challenge myself and risk the possibility of failure and embarrassment as I try to make a small dent in their world.

A special thanks to my parents, Guadalupe and Rebeca Barajas, for bringing me into this world, guiding me, loving me unconditionally, and passing down their best traits. To my two brothers, Jaime Barajas and Joey Barajas, thanks for walking right beside me every step of my life and also for carrying me and reassuring me every time I stumble. Thanks to my sisters, Carly Godinez, Jillian Barajas, and Sarah De La Rosa, for their encouragement and support on my good days and more so on my bad days when I desperately need it.

My cousins, Joanna Barajas, Rosanna Barajas, Guadalupe Arevalo, and Leticia Alcaraz, I am grateful to you for always celebrating my small victories and through your own strength and perseverance, inspiring me to keep pushing forward. Also to my nieces, nephews, and godchildren who turned me into a tía and nina, and at that very moment planted the desire in me to become a better version of myself.

My coaches, Marc and Teresa Hildebrand, thanks for believing in me before I could muster up the courage to believe in myself. Thank you for letting me fly under your wings and for teaching me what it truly means to be a leader.

A special appreciation goes out to Fernando Garcia Barajas and Samantha Urtiz Rivera for helping me edit my Spanish manuscript and making it possible to publish a version that my family can read. My Spanish Edition is dedicated to mamá and papá, my nana, my abuelita, my tias and tios, and to all of you that respond better in the language your heart speaks.

I am filled with so much gratitude when I think of my family and friends, accountability groups, and mastermind teams. Thank you for supporting me along my entire journey. It's because of you that I get up every day feeling so inspired to make a difference. I am unbelievably blessed.

ABOUT THE AUTHOR

After struggling for more than a decade with depression, insomnia, overweight, and low self-worth, Patty Barajas Godinez finally figured out how to live her life with more purpose, learning how to pick up the pieces and put herself back together again.

As Patty discovered the healthy habits that worked for her, she organized them into her own journal, which she realized might help others struggling with the same challenges. Patty loves to see other people rise and expand, and she felt it would be selfish not to share what worked so well for her with the world.

Several years ago, Patty created a growth mindset accountability/mastermind team where she inspires others to take action and live their best life. She has helped hundreds of women who struggle with busy lives, offering them support, accountability, and direction. She is also certified as a Ultimate Portion Fix Nutrition Coach.

Patty has been meal prepping for 10 years for her family. In 2021, after receiving requests for her meals, she founded a local meal preparation business called Blooming Meal Preps.

Patty lives in Castaic, California, with her husband, their three children, and her enormous family. *Keep Going, Keep Growing* is also available in Spanish, Sigue Adelante, Continúa Creciendo.

To learn more, follow Patty's story on Instagram @pbgodinez.